Eleven Plus
Secondary School Selection

Verbal Reasoning

11+
Daily Practice Tests

20 More Tests
Dual Format

Book 3

Introduction

This book is designed to complement the IPS set of verbal reasoning practice papers. It contains short daily practice papers, and uses questions of all of the types covered in the IPS range.

These tests are meant for those who have had some experience of verbal reasoning and the types of questions used.

When practising for tests such as the 11+, or other school entrance exams, most people do not use full length practice papers on a daily basis. However, a few minutes of practice every day can be very beneficial, and it does not put too much strain on the pupil who will sit the exam — which is very important indeed.

Each test should be completed in between five and six minutes. All the question types used in the IPS range of publications are used in this book.

Good luck.

11 Plus Team 2011.

Keep a record of your scores.

Paper	Score:	Paper	Score:
1		11	
2		12	
3		13	
4		14	
5		15	
6		16	
7		17	
8		18	
9		19	
10		20	

Daily Test 1

Question 1

In the question below, the three words in the second group should go together in the same way as the three in the first group. Find the missing word from the second group and write it in the space provided or mark the appropriate box on the multiple choice answer sheet.

untie   [chant]   beach

alert [_____] clash

Question 2

In this question you need to find the number that should appear in the brackets and completes the sum correctly. Write this number in the space provided or mark the appropriate box on the multiple choice answer sheet.

$$3 \times 9 + 8 = 60 \div 4 + (\_\_\_\_)$$

Question 3

In this question the numbers in each group are related in the same way. You must find the missing number in the third group and write it in the space provided or mark the appropriate box on the multiple choice answer sheet.

(8 [57] 7)   (6 [49] 8)

(9 [___] 7)

Question 4

In the sentence below, one word, which is in capitals, has had **three consecutive** letters taken out. These **three** letters will make one correctly spelt word without changing their order. Write the **three-letter** word in the space provided or mark the appropriate box on the multiple choice answer sheet.

Mixing chemicals can cause a dangerous **REION**.

(_____)

Question 5

Below you will see four words and three of their codes. One of the codes is missing. Using the same code, convert the word or number below. Write the answer in the brackets or mark the appropriate box on the multiple choice answer sheet.

HAZE   ZERO   THEM   MARE
4281   5314   6187

Find the code for the word **RAZOR** (_____)

Question 6

In the question below, **one** letter from the word on the left must be moved into the word on the right to make **two** new words. The letters must not be re-arranged. **Both** new words must make sense. Write the correct letter in the space provided or mark the appropriate box on the multiple choice answer sheet.

RUGBY   LOVE   (___)

Question 7

In this question you must find two words, **one** from each group, that are the **closest in meaning**. **Underline** each of these two words or mark the appropriate boxes on the multiple choice answer sheet

(brash   boost   boast)

(brag   brake   brisk)

Question 8

In this question find the **two** words, **one** from each group that will complete the sentence in the best way. **Underline** one word from each group or mark the appropriate boxes on the multiple choice answer sheet.

Match is to (wood, contest, fire)

as rich is to (money, spend, wealthy).

Question 9

In each question below, letters stand for numbers. Work out the answer to the sum and write its **letter** in the brackets or mark the appropriate box on the multiple choice answer sheet.

A = 4, B = 8, C = 16, D = 12, E = 10,

B + C - A - D = (___)

Question 10

A B C D E F G H I J K L M N O P Q R S T U V W X Y Z

In this question a word has been written in code. An example has been worked out for you. You must now work out the missing word using the same code. Write the word in the space provided or mark the appropriate box on the multiple choice answer sheet.

If the code for **THEY** is **VKID**

what does **YDHJ** mean? (_____)

Daily Test 2

Question 1

In the question below, find one letter that will complete the word in front of the brackets and begin the word after the brackets.
The same letter must fit into both sets of brackets.
Write the letter on the answer sheet or mark the appropriate box on the multiple choice answer sheet.

FLA (___) ASH : SNO (___) EST

Question 2

In this question you need to find the number that should appear in the brackets and will continue the series in the most sensible way. Write this number in the space provided or mark the appropriate box on the multiple choice answer sheet.

110,   125,   140,   155,   170,   (____)

Question 3

In the sentence below, a word of four letters is hidden at the end of one word and the beginning of the next word.
Underline the **pair** of words that contain the hidden word or mark the appropriate box on the multiple choice answer sheet.

Magicians often use special playing cards.

Question 4

A B C D E F G H I J K L M N O P Q R S T U V W X Y Z

In the question below, find the pair of letters that will complete the sentence in the best way and write the correct answer in the answer box or mark the appropriate box on the multiple choice answer sheet.

GA is to **CB**

as **NJ** is to (_____)

Question 5

In the question below, there are two pairs of words. You must find the word from the list that will go equally well with both pairs of words in the brackets.
Underline this word or mark the appropriate box on the multiple choice answer sheet.

NEXT   HOT   WARM   BESIDE   CLOSE

(MUGGY   HUMID)   (NEAR   ADJOINING)

Question 6

In this question there are three pairs of words. You must complete the third pair in the same way as the first two pairs. Write the correct word in the space provided or mark the appropriate box on the multiple choice answer sheet.

(snore, one)   (blade, ale)

(later, _____)

Question 7

In the question below, find two words, **one** from each group, that are the **most opposite in meaning**.
Underline each of these two words or mark the appropriate boxes on the multiple choice answer sheet

(bury   dig   empty)

(rake   unearth   burrow)

Question 8

In the question below, find the **two** words that are **different** from the other three and **underline** them on the answer sheet or mark the appropriate box on the multiple choice answer sheet.

swamp   flood   bog   marsh   reed

Question 9

A B C D E F G H I J K L M N O P Q R S T U V W X Y Z

In this question you need to find the pair of letters that will complete the sequence in the best way and write the correct answer in the answer box or mark the appropriate box on the multiple choice answer sheet.

FW,   HY,   JA,   LC,   NE,   (_____)

Question 10

In the question below, choose **two** words, **one** from each set, that will together make **one** correctly spelt word. You may not change the order of the letters.
The word from the set on the top always comes first.
Underline the two words or mark the appropriate boxes on the multiple choice answer sheet.

(by   can   at)

(end   tack   type)

Daily Test 3

Question 1

In the question below, the three words in the second group should go together in the same way as the three in the first group. Find the missing word from the second group and write it in the space provided or mark the appropriate box on the multiple choice answer sheet.

start   [reach]   cheer

cleft   [_____]   shrub

Question 2

In this question you need to find the number that should appear in the brackets and completes the sum correctly. Write this number in the space provided or mark the appropriate box on the multiple choice answer sheet.

12 x 5 x 2 = 59 + 33 + (_____)

Question 3

In this question the numbers in each group are related in the same way. You must find the missing number in the third group and write it in the space provided or mark the appropriate box on the multiple choice answer sheet.

(18 [20] 38)   (19 [27] 46)

(17 [____] 40)

Question 4

In the sentence below, one word, which is in capitals, has had **three consecutive** letters taken out. These **three** letters will make one correctly spelt word without changing their order. Write the **three-letter** word in the space provided or mark the appropriate box on the multiple choice answer sheet.

The girls always wanted to **PERM** on stage.

(_____)

Question 5

Below you will see four words and three of their codes. One of the codes is missing. Using the same code, convert the word or number below. Write the answer in the brackets or mark the appropriate box on the multiple choice answer sheet.

LAKE   CALM   ROCK   SEAL

3641   2587   1476

Find the code for the word **COOLER** (_____)

Question 6

In the question below, **one** letter from the word on the left must be moved into the word on the right to make **two** new words. The letters must not be re-arranged. **Both** new words must make sense. Write the correct letter in the space provided or mark the appropriate box on the multiple choice answer sheet.

PEDAL   WELL   (____)

Question 7

In this question you must find two words, **one** from each group, that are the **closest in meaning**. **Underline** each of these two words or mark the appropriate boxes on the multiple choice answer sheet

(game   winner   result)

(loser   monopoly   outcome)

Question 8

In this question find the **two** words, **one** from each group that will complete the sentence in the best way. **Underline** one word from each group or mark the appropriate boxes on the multiple choice answer sheet.

Devil is to (horns, lived, red)

as drawer is to (reward, chest, artist).

Question 9

In each question below, letters stand for numbers. Work out the answer to the sum and write its **letter** in the brackets or mark the appropriate box on the multiple choice answer sheet.

A = 27, B = 9, C = 15, D = 5, E = 3,

D x E + C - A = (____)

Question 10

A B C D E F G H I J K L M N O P Q R S T U V W X Y Z

In this question a word has been written in code. An example has been worked out for you. You must now work out the missing word using the same code. Write the word in the space provided or mark the appropriate box on the multiple choice answer sheet.

If the code for **DOWN** is **EPXO**,

what is the code for **DUCK**? (_____)

Daily Test 4

Question 1

In the question below, find one letter that will complete the word in front of the brackets and begin the word after the brackets.
The same letter must fit into both sets of brackets.
Write the letter on the answer sheet or mark the appropriate box on the multiple choice answer sheet.

SEE (___) EEP   :   LEA (___) UEL

Question 2

In this question you need to find the number that should appear in the brackets and will continue the series in the most sensible way. Write this number in the space provided or mark the appropriate box on the multiple choice answer sheet.

1,   3,   6,   8,   16,   18,   (____)

Question 3

In the sentence below, a word of four letters is hidden at the end of one word and the beginning of the next word.
Underline the **pair** of words that contain the hidden word or mark the appropriate box on the multiple choice answer sheet.

Mandy's biscuits were crisp and sweet.

Question 4

A B C D E F G H I J K L M N O P Q R S T U V W X Y Z

In the question below, find the pair of letters that will complete the sentence in the best way and write the correct answer in the answer box or mark the appropriate box on the multiple choice answer sheet.

ST is to **TX**
    as **UW** is to (_____)

Question 5

In the question below, there are two pairs of words. You must find the word from the list that will go equally well with both pairs of words in the brackets.
Underline this word or mark the appropriate box on the multiple choice answer sheet.

COMB   SEEK   FIND   UNRAVEL   ARRANGE

(HUNT   SEARCH)   (UNTANGLE   BRUSH)

Question 6

In this question there are three pairs of words. You must complete the third pair in the same way as the first two pairs. Write the correct word in the space provided or mark the appropriate box on the multiple choice answer sheet.

(arena, near)   (tripe, pier)

(heart, _____)

Question 7

In the question below, find two words, **one** from each group, that are the **most opposite in meaning**.
Underline each of these two words or mark the appropriate boxes on the multiple choice answer sheet

(provide   project   proceed)
(stake   stop   stifle)

Question 8

In the question below, find the **two** words that are **different** from the other three and **underline** them on the answer sheet or mark the appropriate box on the multiple choice answer sheet.

fix   make   attach   fasten   repair

Question 9

A B C D E F G H I J K L M N O P Q R S T U V W X Y Z

In this question you need to find the pair of letters that will complete the sequence in the best way and write the correct answer in the answer box or mark the appropriate box on the multiple choice answer sheet.

RZ,   QB,   OD,   LF,   HH,   (_____)

Question 10

In the question below, choose **two** words, **one** from each set, that will together make **one** correctly spelt word. You may not change the order of the letters.
The word from the set on the top always comes first.
Underline the two words or mark the appropriate boxes on the multiple choice answer sheet.

(tame   straw   fin)
(gcar   dust   berry)

Daily Test 5

Question 1

In this question there are three pairs of words. You must complete the third pair in the same way as the first two pairs. Write the correct word in the space provided or mark the appropriate box on the multiple choice answer sheet.

(palace, pale)   (rotate, rate)

(belated, _____)

Question 2

In the question below, find two words, **one** from each group, that are the **most opposite in meaning**. **Underline** each of these two words or mark the appropriate boxes on the multiple choice answer sheet

(expect   exact   accept)

(delay   partly   refuse)

Question 3

In the question below, find the **two** words that are **different** from the other three and **underline** them on the answer sheet or mark the appropriate box on the multiple choice answer sheet.

tooth   hole   cavity   dentist   pit

Question 4

A B C D E F G H I J K L M N O P Q R S T U V W X Y Z

In this question you need to find the pair of letters that will complete the sequence in the best way and write the correct answer in the answer box or mark the appropriate box on the multiple choice answer sheet.

KD, HE, EG, BJ, YN, (_____)

Question 5

In the question below, choose **two** words, **one** from each set, that will together make **one** correctly spelt word. You may not change the order of the letters. The word from the set on the top always comes first. **Underline** the two words or mark the appropriate boxes on the multiple choice answer sheet.

(house   flat   even)

(tend   warm   hold)

Question 6

In the question below, find one letter that will complete the word in front of the brackets and begin the word after the brackets. **The same letter must fit into both sets of brackets.** Write the letter between the brackets on the sheet or mark the appropriate box on the multiple choice answer sheet.

BEA (___) OWN   :   SIL (___) EAR

Question 7

In this question you need to find the number that should appear in the brackets and will continue the series in the most sensible way. Write this number in the space provided or mark the appropriate box on the multiple choice answer sheet.

28,   28,   31,   27,   34,   26,   (____)

Question 8

In the sentence below, a word of four letters is hidden at the end of one word and the beginning of the next word. **Underline** the **pair** of words that contain the hidden word or mark the appropriate box on the multiple choice answer sheet.

The loud music kept everyone awake.

Question 9

A B C D E F G H I J K L M N O P Q R S T U V W X Y Z

In the question below, find the pair of letters that will complete the sentence in the best way and write the correct answer in the answer box or mark the appropriate box on the multiple choice answer sheet.

CI is to **ZF**

as **GK** is to (_____)

Question 10

In the question below, there are two pairs of words. You must find the word from the list that will go equally well with both pairs of words in the brackets. **Underline** this word or mark the appropriate box on the multiple choice answer sheet.

WASP   FASTEN   BOLT   EXIT   GRAB

(LOCK   CATCH)   (FLEE   FLY)

Daily Test 6

Question 1

In the question below, **one** letter from the word on the left must be moved into the word on the right to make **two** new words. The letters must not be re-arranged.
Both new words must make sense.
Write the correct letter in the space provided or mark the appropriate box on the multiple choice answer sheet.

SHAME   SIRE   (___)

Question 2

In this question you must find two words, **one** from each group, that are the **closest in meaning**.
Underline each of these two words or mark the appropriate boxes on the multiple choice answer sheet

(notice   sign   placard)

(spot   slip   split)

Question 3

In this question find the **two** words, **one** from each group that will complete the sentence in the best way.
Underline one word from each group or mark the appropriate boxes on the multiple choice answer sheet.

Herd is to (heard, cattle, pasture)

as flock is to (sheep, group, fleck).

Question 4

In each question below, letters stand for numbers. Work out the answer to the sum and write its **letter** in the brackets or mark the appropriate box on the multiple choice answer sheet.

A = 20, B = 10, C = 5, D = 50, E = 3,

D ÷ B x E + C = (___)

Question 5

A B C D E F G H I J K L M N O P Q R S T U V W X Y Z

In this question a word has been written in code. An example has been worked out for you. You must now work out the missing word in the same way. Write the word in the space provided or mark the appropriate box on the multiple choice answer sheet.

If the code for **VINE** is **ZERA**,

what does **TKPA** mean? (_____)

Question 6

In the question below, the three words in the second group should go together in the same way as the three in the first group. Find the missing word from the second group and write it in the space provided or mark the appropriate box on the multiple choice answer sheet.

taste   [steam]   marks

metre [_____] sense

Question 7

In this question you need to find the number that should appear in the brackets and completes the sum correctly. Write this number in the space provided or mark the appropriate box on the multiple choice answer sheet.

16 + 17 + 18 = 3 x 17 + (_____)

Question 8

In this question the numbers in each group are related in the same way. You must find the missing number in the third group and write it in the space provided or mark the appropriate box on the multiple choice answer sheet.

(50 [20] 10)   (45 [15] 15)

(48 [____] 20)

Question 9

In the sentence below, one word, which is in capitals, has had **three consecutive** letters taken out. These **three** letters will make one correctly spelt word without changing their order. Write the **three-letter** word in the space provided or mark the appropriate box on the multiple choice answer sheet.

My brothers always **DIREE** over who's better at chess.

(_____)

Question 10

Below you will see four words and three of their codes. One of the codes is missing. Using the same code, convert the word or number below. Write the answer in the brackets or mark the appropriate box on the multiple choice answer sheet.

SHIP   DESK   HIDE   CASE
9813   4315   2743

Find the word for the code **1574434** (_____)

Daily Test 7

Question 1

In the question below, find one letter that will complete the word in front of the brackets and begin the word after the brackets.
The same letter must fit into both sets of brackets.
Write the letter on the answer sheet or mark the appropriate box on the multiple choice answer sheet.

COR (___) ILL : LIN (___) NEE

Question 2

In this question you need to find the number that should appear in the brackets and will continue the series in the most sensible way. Write this number in the space provided or mark the appropriate box on the multiple choice answer sheet.

13, 14, 16, 19, 23, 28, (____)

Question 3

In the sentence below, a word of four letters is hidden at the end of one word and the beginning of the next word.
Underline the **pair** of words that contain the hidden word or mark the appropriate box on the multiple choice answer sheet.

Andrew's English homework was quite messy..

Question 4

A B C D E F G H I J K L M N O P Q R S T U V W X Y Z

In the question below, find the pair of letters that will complete the sentence in the best way and write the correct answer in the answer box or mark the appropriate box on the multiple choice answer sheet.

EW is to **GU**

as **TF** is to (_____)

Question 5

In the question below, there are two pairs of words. You must find the word from the list that will go equally well with both pairs of words in the brackets.
Underline this word or mark the appropriate box on the multiple choice answer sheet.

LONELY LEAK STRAIN EMPTY PLAIN

(DESERTED BARE) (DRAIN UNLOAD)

Question 6

In this question there are three pairs of words. You must complete the third pair in the same way as the first two pairs. Write the correct word in the space provided or mark the appropriate box on the multiple choice answer sheet.

(narrate, rant) (damaged, made)

(pirates, _____)

Question 7

In the question below, find two words, **one** from each group, that are the **most opposite in meaning**.
Underline each of these two words or mark the appropriate boxes on the multiple choice answer sheet

(testify magnify purify)

(reduce reflect remote)

Question 8

In the question below, find the **two** words that are **different** from the other three and **underline** them on the answer sheet or mark the appropriate box on the multiple choice answer sheet.

perfect faceless perform flawless faultless

Question 9

A B C D E F G H I J K L M N O P Q R S T U V W X Y Z

In this question you need to find the pair of letters that will complete the sequence in the best way and write the correct answer in the answer box or mark the appropriate box on the multiple choice answer sheet.

KH, IK, GN, EQ, CT, (_____)

Question 10

In the question below, choose **two** words, **one** from each set, that will together make **one** correctly spelt word. You may not change the order of the letters.
The word from the set on the top always comes first.
Underline the two words or mark the appropriate boxes on the multiple choice answer sheet.

(ours their your)

(elves imps fairies)

Daily Test 8

Score. _____

Question 1

In the question below, **one** letter from the word on the left must be moved into the word on the right to make **two** new words. The letters must not be re-arranged. **Both** new words must make sense.

Write the correct letter in the space provided or mark the appropriate box on the multiple choice answer sheet.

RANGE   SORE   (_____)

Question 2

In this question you must find two words, **one** from each group, that are the **closest in meaning**.

Underline each of these two words or mark the appropriate boxes on the multiple choice answer sheet

(ring   knock   call)

(sink   plug   tap)

Question 3

In this question find the **two** words, **one** from each group that will complete the sentence in the best way.

Underline one word from each group or mark the appropriate boxes on the multiple choice answer sheet.

Mail is to (envelope, male, postman)

as pail is to (bucket, pale, white).

Question 4

In each question below, letters stand for numbers. Work out the answer to the sum and write its **letter** in the brackets or mark the appropriate box on the multiple choice answer sheet.

A = 100, B = 5, C = 50, D = 125, E = 25,

A - C + E - C = (_____)

Question 5

A B C D E F G H I J K L M N O P Q R S T U V W X Y Z

In this question a word has been written in code. An example has been worked out for you. You must now work out the missing code in the same way. Write the code in the space provided or mark the appropriate box on the multiple choice answer sheet.

If **SJDLNQ** means **PLANKS**,

what is the code for **WOODEN**?

(_____)

Question 6

In the question below, the three words in the second group should go together in the same way as the three in the first group. Find the missing word from the second group and write it in the space provided or mark the appropriate box on the multiple choice answer sheet.

dream   [ready]   dairy

scare [_____] dents

Question 7

In this question you need to find the number that should appear in the brackets and completes the sum correctly. Write this number in the space provided or mark the appropriate box on the multiple choice answer sheet.

3 x 4 x 5 = 50 + 47 - (_____)

Question 8

In this question the numbers in each group are related in the same way. You must find the missing number in the third group and write it in the space provided or mark the appropriate box on the multiple choice answer sheet.

(3 [11] 3)   (4 [14] 3)

(4 [____] 5)

Question 9

In the sentence below, one word, which is in capitals, has had **three consecutive** letters taken out. These **three** letters will make one correctly spelt word without changing their order. Write the **three-letter** word in the space provided or mark the appropriate box on the multiple choice answer sheet.

Jenny and Sam wrote an **ICLE** about fashion.

(_____)

Question 10

Below you will see four words and three of their codes. One of the codes is missing. Using the same code, convert the word or number below. Write the answer in the brackets or mark the appropriate box on the multiple choice answer sheet.

BARK   ROBE   BEAR   KITE
8715   2697   8152

Find the word for the code **85712**   (_____)

Daily Test 9

Question 1

In the question below, the three words in the second group should go together in the same way as the three in the first group. Find the missing word from the second group and write it in the space provided or mark the appropriate box on the multiple choice answer sheet.

snore   [chest]   teach

metre [_____] earth

Question 2

In this question you need to find the number that should appear in the brackets and completes the sum correctly. Write this number in the space provided or mark the appropriate box on the multiple choice answer sheet.

$10 \times 10 \div 2 = 6 \times 7 + (\_\_\_\_)$

Question 3

In this question the numbers in each group are related in the same way. You must find the missing number in the third group and write it in the space provided or mark the appropriate box on the multiple choice answer sheet.

(23 [44] 18)   (19 [35] 13)

(14 [___] 15)

Question 4

In the sentence below, one word, which is in capitals, has had **three consecutive** letters taken out. These **three** letters will make one correctly spelt word without changing their order. Write the **three-letter** word in the space provided or mark the appropriate box on the multiple choice answer sheet.

You will improve if you **PRICE** every day.

(_____)

Question 5

Below you will see four words and three of their codes. One of the codes is missing. Using the same code, convert the word or number below. Write the answer in the brackets or mark the appropriate box on the multiple choice answer sheet.

FISH   PEAS   CHIP   SHOP

8461   7491   1257

Find the code for the word **SPACE**   (_____)

Question 6

In the question below, **one** letter from the word on the left must be moved into the word on the right to make **two** new words. The letters must not be re-arranged. **Both** new words must make sense. Write the correct letter in the space provided or mark the appropriate box on the multiple choice answer sheet.

SPLIT   GROW   (____)

Question 7

In this question you must find two words, **one** from each group, that are the **closest in meaning**. **Underline** each of these two words or mark the appropriate boxes on the multiple choice answer sheet

(pledge   plead   question)

(respond   promise   require)

Question 8

In this question find the **two** words, **one** from each group that will complete the sentence in the best way. **Underline** one word from each group or mark the appropriate boxes on the multiple choice answer sheet.

Spoke is to (wheel, bicycle, speak)

as laid is to (lay, down, egg).

Question 9

In each question below, letters stand for numbers. Work out the answer to the sum and write its **letter** in the brackets or mark the appropriate box on the multiple choice answer sheet.

A = 24, B = 36, C = 3, D = 8, E = 2,

$B \div E + C + C = (\_\_\_\_)$

Question 10

A B C D E F G H I J K L M N O P Q R S T U V W X Y Z

In this question a word has been written in code. An example has been worked out for you. You must now work out the missing word using the same code. Write the word in the space provided or mark the appropriate box on the multiple choice answer sheet.

If the code for **BEGAN** is **YBDXK**

What is the code for **AWFUL**? (_____)

Question 1

In the question below, find one letter that will complete the word in front of the brackets and begin the word after the brackets.
The same letter must fit into both sets of brackets.
Write the letter on the answer sheet or mark the appropriate box on the multiple choice answer sheet.

DUN (___) NAW   :   LON (___) ATE

Question 2

In this question you need to find the number that should appear in the brackets and will continue the series in the most sensible way. Write this number in the space provided or mark the appropriate box on the multiple choice answer sheet.

1,   2,   3,   5,   8,   13,   (____)

Question 3

In the sentence below, a word of four letters is hidden at the end of one word and the beginning of the next word.
Underline the **pair** of words that contain the hidden word or mark the appropriate box on the multiple choice answer sheet.

Thick snow covered those mountain tops.

Question 4

A B C D E F G H I J K L M N O P Q R S T U V W X Y Z

In the question below, find the pair of letters that will complete the sentence in the best way and write the correct answer in the answer box or mark the appropriate box on the multiple choice answer sheet.

GQ is to **ER**
as **QG** is to (_____)

Question 5

In the question below, there are two pairs of words. You must find the word from the list that will go equally well with both pairs of words in the brackets.
Underline this word or mark the appropriate box on the multiple choice answer sheet.

FIX   RECTIFY   NAIL   SORT   RESTORE

(ATTACH   STICK) (MEND   REPAIR)

Question 6

In this question there are three pairs of words. You must complete the third pair in the same way as the first two pairs. Write the correct word in the space provided or mark the appropriate box on the multiple choice answer sheet.

(flake, flame)   (crate, crave)

(stare, _____)

Question 7

In the question below, find two words, **one** from each group, that are the **most opposite in meaning**.
Underline each of these two words or mark the appropriate boxes on the multiple choice answer sheet

(hesitant   ignorant   certain)
(direct   decisive   defiant)

Question 8

In the question below, find the **two** words that are **different** from the other three and **underline** them on the answer sheet or mark the appropriate box on the multiple choice answer sheet.

sweet   rich   prosperous   dessert   wealthy

Question 9

A B C D E F G H I J K L M N O P Q R S T U V W X Y Z

In this question you need to find the pair of letters that will complete the sequence in the best way and write the correct answer in the answer box or mark the appropriate box on the multiple choice answer sheet.

GF,   FI,   EL,   DO,   CR,   (_____)

Question 10

In the question below, choose **two** words, **one** from each set, that will together make **one** correctly spelt word. You may not change the order of the letters.
The word from the set on the top always comes first.
Underline the two words or mark the appropriate boxes on the multiple choice answer sheet.

(rode   way   lane)
(word   ward   work)

Daily Test 11

Question 1

In the question below, the three words in the second group should go together in the same way as the three in the first group. Find the missing word from the second group and write it in the space provided or mark the appropriate box on the multiple choice answer sheet.

cloth   [catch]   actor

fried   [_____]   inlet

Question 2

In this question you need to find the number that should appear in the brackets and completes the sum correctly. Write this number in the space provided or mark the appropriate box on the multiple choice answer sheet.

$$48 \div 2 \div 3 \ = \ 30 - 17 - (\_\_\_)$$

Question 3

In this question the numbers in each group are related in the same way. You must find the missing number in the third group and write it in the space provided or mark the appropriate box on the multiple choice answer sheet.

(16 [22] 5)   (18 [16] 10)

(30 [___] 14)

Question 4

In the sentence below, one word, which is in capitals, has had **three consecutive** letters taken out. These **three** letters will make one correctly spelt word without changing their order. Write the **three-letter** word in the space provided or mark the appropriate box on the multiple choice answer sheet.

There is a **GER** in the sett over there.

(_____)

Question 5

Below you will see four words and three of their codes. One of the codes is missing. Using the same code, convert the word or number below. Write the answer in the brackets or mark the appropriate box on the multiple choice answer sheet.

KITE   BEAR   ROBE   BARK
2697   8715   8152

Find the code for the word **BEATER** (_____)

Question 6

In the question below, **one** letter from the word on the left must be moved into the word on the right to make **two** new words. The letters must not be re-arranged. **Both** new words must make sense. Write the correct letter in the space provided or mark the appropriate box on the multiple choice answer sheet.

BLEND   SAKE   (___)

Question 7

In this question you must find two words, **one** from each group, that are the **closest in meaning**. **Underline** each of these two words or mark the appropriate boxes on the multiple choice answer sheet

(tumble   mount   peak)
(clench   valley   climb)

Question 8

In this question find the **two** words, **one** from each group that will complete the sentence in the best way. **Underline** one word from each group or mark the appropriate boxes on the multiple choice answer sheet.

Doctor is to (nurse, practice, hospital)

as teacher is to (pupil, professor, school).

Question 9

In each question below, letters stand for numbers. Work out the answer to the sum and write its **letter** in the brackets or mark the appropriate box on the multiple choice answer sheet.

A = 2,   B = 10,   C = 3,   D = 15,   E = 5,

$$B \times D \div E \div B = \ (\_\_\_)$$

Question 10

A B C D E F G H I J K L M N O P Q R S T U V W X Y Z

In this question a word has been written in code. An example has been worked out for you. You must now work out the missing word using the same code. Write the word in the space provided or mark the appropriate box on the multiple choice answer sheet.

If the code for **POEM** is **TSIQ**,

what does **WSRK** mean? (_____)

Daily Test 12

Question 1

In the question below, find one letter that will complete the word in front of the brackets and begin the word after the brackets.
The same letter must fit into both sets of brackets.
Write the letter on the answer sheet or mark the appropriate box on the multiple choice answer sheet.

GRI (___) ALE : SLA (___) ANT

Question 2

In this question you need to find the number that should appear in the brackets and will continue the series in the most sensible way. Write this number in the space provided or mark the appropriate box on the multiple choice answer sheet.

3, 4, 7, 11, 18, 29, (____)

Question 3

In the sentence below, a word of four letters is hidden at the end of one word and the beginning of the next word.
Underline the **pair** of words that contain the hidden word or mark the appropriate box on the multiple choice answer sheet.

The sailor drifted across the ocean.

Question 4

A B C D E F G H I J K L M N O P Q R S T U V W X Y Z

In the question below, find the pair of letters that will complete the sentence in the best way and write the correct answer in the answer box or mark the appropriate box on the multiple choice answer sheet.

IV is to **MU**

as **LQ** is to (_____)

Question 5

In the question below, there are two pairs of words. You must find the word from the list that will go equally well with both pairs of words in the brackets.
Underline this word or mark the appropriate box on the multiple choice answer sheet.

SINK   TROUBLED   TORMENT   UPSET   DROOP

(TOPPLE   CAPSIZE) (DISTRESSED   DISTURBED)

Question 6

In this question there are three pairs of words. You must complete the third pair in the same way as the first two pairs. Write the correct word in the space provided or mark the appropriate box on the multiple choice answer sheet.

(regret, greet)   (pastel, steal)

(metals, _____)

Question 7

In the question below, find two words, **one** from each group, that are the **most opposite in meaning**.
Underline each of these two words or mark the appropriate boxes on the multiple choice answer sheet

(clumsy   lenient   erratic)

(awkward   severe   honest)

Question 8

In the question below, find the **two** words that are **different** from the other three and **underline** them on the answer sheet or mark the appropriate box on the multiple choice answer sheet.

diamond   silver   gold   ruby   emerald

Question 9

A B C D E F G H I J K L M N O P Q R S T U V W X Y Z

In this question you need to find the pair of letters that will complete the sequence in the best way and write the correct answer in the answer box or mark the appropriate box on the multiple choice answer sheet.

DF, AG, XI, UJ, RL, (_____)

Question 10

In the question below, choose **two** words, **one** from each set, that will together make **one** correctly spelt word. You may not change the order of the letters.
The word from the set on the top always comes first.
Underline the two words or mark the appropriate boxes on the multiple choice answer sheet.

(per over run)

(face chase fume)

Daily Test 13

Question 1

In this question there are three pairs of words. You must complete the third pair in the same way as the first two pairs. Write the correct word in the space provided or mark the appropriate box on the multiple choice answer sheet.

(disused, side)   (divider, dire)

(caskets, _____)

Question 2

In the question below, find two words, **one** from each group, that are the **most opposite in meaning**.
Underline each of these two words or mark the appropriate boxes on the multiple choice answer sheet

(ready   steady   charge)

(unstable   fixed   faulty)

Question 3

In the question below, find the **two** words that are **different** from the other three and **underline** them on the answer sheet or mark the appropriate box on the multiple choice answer sheet.

melt   boil   defrost   heat   thaw

Question 4

A B C D E F G H I J K L M N O P Q R S T U V W X Y Z

In this question you need to find the pair of letters that will complete the sequence in the best way and write the correct answer in the answer box or mark the appropriate box on the multiple choice answer sheet.

EU,   AQ,   DT,   ZP,   CS,   (_____)

Question 5

In the question below, choose **two** words, **one** from each set, that will together make **one** correctly spelt word. You may not change the order of the letters.
The word from the set on the top always comes first.
Underline the two words or mark the appropriate boxes on the multiple choice answer sheet.

(break   snap   cut)

(though   through   tough)

Question 6

In the question below, find one letter that will complete the word in front of the brackets and begin the word after the brackets.
The same letter must fit into both sets of brackets.
Write the letter between the brackets on the sheet or mark the appropriate box on the multiple choice answer sheet.

BUR (___) EAR   :   FLO (___) IER

Question 7

In this question you need to find the number that should appear in the brackets and will continue the series in the most sensible way. Write this number in the space provided or mark the appropriate box on the multiple choice answer sheet.

275,   265,   245,   215,   175,   (____)

Question 8

In the sentence below, a word of four letters is hidden at the end of one word and the beginning of the next word. **Underline** the **pair** of words that contain the hidden word or mark the appropriate box on the multiple choice answer sheet.

Keep calm when the alarm rings.

Question 9

A B C D E F G H I J K L M N O P Q R S T U V W X Y Z

In the question below, find the pair of letters that will complete the sentence in the best way and write the correct answer in the answer box or mark the appropriate box on the multiple choice answer sheet.

GB is to **DZ**

as **NK** is to (_____)

Question 10

In the question below, there are two pairs of words. You must find the word from the list that will go equally well with both pairs of words in the brackets.
Underline this word or mark the appropriate box on the multiple choice answer sheet.

ATTACHED   SPRING   SKIP   BONDED   BOUND

(LEAP   JUMP)   (TIED   TETHERED)

Daily Test 14

Question 1

In the question below, **one** letter from the word on the left must be moved into the word on the right to make **two** new words. The letters must not be re-arranged.
Both new words must make sense.
Write the correct letter in the space provided or mark the appropriate box on the multiple choice answer sheet.

LANCE   AREA   (____)

Question 2

In this question you must find two words, **one** from each group, that are the **closest in meaning**.
Underline each of these two words or mark the appropriate boxes on the multiple choice answer sheet

(mystery   confess   mimic)

(confuse   puzzle   mystify)

Question 3

In this question find the **two** words, **one** from each group that will complete the sentence in the best way.
Underline one word from each group or mark the appropriate boxes on the multiple choice answer sheet.

Cease is to (crease, grab, start)

as cheap is to (dear, heap, bird).

Question 4

In each question below, letters stand for numbers. Work out the answer to the sum and write its **letter** in the brackets or mark the appropriate box on the multiple choice answer sheet.

A = 3,   B = 7,   C = 12,   D = 4,   E = 15,

D x E ÷ C + B = (____)

Question 5

A B C D E F G H I J K L M N O P Q R S T U V W X Y Z

In this question a word has been written in code. An example has been worked out for you. You must now work out the missing code in the same way. Write the code in the space provided or mark the appropriate box on the multiple choice answer sheet.

If **BZVJKM** means **VERMIN**,

what is the code for **OCEANS**?

(_____)

Question 6

In the question below, the three words in the second group should go together in the same way as the three in the first group. Find the missing word from the second group and write it in the space provided or mark the appropriate box on the multiple choice answer sheet.

limit   [miles]   bless

disco   [_____]   cared

Question 7

In this question you need to find the number that should appear in the brackets and completes the sum correctly. Write this number in the space provided or mark the appropriate box on the multiple choice answer sheet.

81 ÷ 9 - 2   =   40 ÷ 2 - (_____)

Question 8

In this question the numbers in each group are related in the same way. You must find the missing number in the third group and write it in the space provided or mark the appropriate box on the multiple choice answer sheet.

(17 [30] 18)   (26 [49] 28)

(14 [____] 36)

Question 9

In the sentence below, one word, which is in capitals, has had **three consecutive** letters taken out. These **three** letters will make one correctly spelt word without changing their order. Write the **three-letter** word in the space provided or mark the appropriate box on the multiple choice answer sheet.

The skater **GED** gracefully across the ice.

(____)

Question 10

Below you will see four words and three of their codes. One of the codes is missing. Using the same code, convert the word or number below. Write the answer in the brackets or mark the appropriate box on the multiple choice answer sheet.

THEM   ZERO   MARE   HAZE
5314   4281   6187

Find the word for the code   **475318**   (_____)

Daily Test 15

Question 1

In the question below, find one letter that will complete the word in front of the brackets and begin the word after the brackets.
The same letter must fit into both sets of brackets.
Write the letter on the answer sheet or mark the appropriate box on the multiple choice answer sheet.

DEA (___) AST   :   MAI (___) ATE

Question 2

In this question you need to find the number that should appear in the brackets and will continue the series in the most sensible way. Write this number in the space provided or mark the appropriate box on the multiple choice answer sheet.

12,   15,   19,   22,   26,   29,   (____)

Question 3

In the sentence below, a word of four letters is hidden at the end of one word and the beginning of the next word.
Underline the **pair** of words that contain the hidden word or mark the appropriate box on the multiple choice answer sheet.

Some genies live inside old lamps.

Question 4

A B C D E F G H I J K L M N O P Q R S T U V W X Y Z

In the question below, find the pair of letters that will complete the sentence in the best way and write the correct answer in the answer box or mark the appropriate box on the multiple choice answer sheet.

CH is to EJ

as EJ is to (_____)

Question 5

In the question below, there are two pairs of words. You must find the word from the list that will go equally well with both pairs of words in the brackets.
Underline this word or mark the appropriate box on the multiple choice answer sheet.

STRIP   FIGHT   STRING   ROW   QUEUE

(ARGUE   QUARREL) (LINE   COLUMN)

Question 6

In this question there are three pairs of words. You must complete the third pair in the same way as the first two pairs. Write the correct word in the space provided or mark the appropriate box on the multiple choice answer sheet.

(least, mast)   (shank, tank)

(blame, _____)

Question 7

In the question below, find two words, **one** from each group, that are the **most opposite in meaning**.
Underline each of these two words or mark the appropriate boxes on the multiple choice answer sheet

(bright   occupy   seldom)

(often   rare   quietly)

Question 8

In the question below, find the **two** words that are **different** from the other three and **underline** them on the answer sheet or mark the appropriate box on the multiple choice answer sheet.

begin   end   start   finish   conclude

Question 9

A B C D E F G H I J K L M N O P Q R S T U V W X Y Z

In this question you need to find the pair of letters that will complete the sequence in the best way and write the correct answer in the answer box or mark the appropriate box on the multiple choice answer sheet.

JK,   KM,   LO,   MQ,   NS,   (_____)

Question 10

In the question below, choose **two** words, **one** from each set, that will together make **one** correctly spelt word. You may not change the order of the letters.
The word from the set on the top always comes first.
Underline the two words or mark the appropriate boxes on the multiple choice answer sheet.

(short   rum   flow)

(wing   age   here)

Daily Test 16

Question 1

In the question below, **one** letter from the word on the left must be moved into the word on the right to make **two** new words. The letters must not be re-arranged. **Both** new words must make sense.
Write the correct letter in the space provided or mark the appropriate box on the multiple choice answer sheet.

HEART   MOOR   (_____)

Question 2

In this question you must find two words, **one** from each group, that are the **closest in meaning**.
Underline each of these two words or mark the appropriate boxes on the multiple choice answer sheet

(remind   remove   remedy)

(placed   cure   behind)

Question 3

In this question find the **two** words, **one** from each group that will complete the sentence in the best way.
Underline one word from each group or mark the appropriate boxes on the multiple choice answer sheet.

Pick is to (mix, choose, shovel)

as move is to (shift, house, motivate).

Question 4

In each question below, letters stand for numbers. Work out the answer to the sum and write its **letter** in the brackets or mark the appropriate box on the multiple choice answer sheet.

A = 4, B = 11, C = 7, D = 21, E = 3,

C x E - D + A = (____)

Question 5

A B C D E F G H I J K L M N O P Q R S T U V W X Y Z

In this question a word has been written in code. An example has been worked out for you. You must now work out the missing code in the same way. Write the code in the space provided or mark the appropriate box on the multiple choice answer sheet.

If the code for **SHAFT** is **PIXGQ**,

what does **JJKFO** mean? (_____)

Question 6

In the question below, the three words in the second group should go together in the same way as the three in the first group. Find the missing word from the second group and write it in the space provided or mark the appropriate box on the multiple choice answer sheet.

blame   [cable]   clean

adore   [_____]   tears

Question 7

In this question you need to find the number that should appear in the brackets and completes the sum correctly. Write this number in the space provided or mark the appropriate box on the multiple choice answer sheet.

16 + 15 + 14 = 13 + 17 + (_____)

Question 8

In this question the numbers in each group are related in the same way. You must find the missing number in the third group and write it in the space provided or mark the appropriate box on the multiple choice answer sheet.

(9 [60] 7)   (8 [77] 10)

(6 [____] 9)

Question 9

In the sentence below, one word, which is in capitals, has had **three consecutive** letters taken out. These **three** letters will make one correctly spelt word without changing their order. Write the **three-letter** word in the space provided or mark the appropriate box on the multiple choice answer sheet.

The waiter looked like a **GUIN** in his black suit.

(_____)

Question 10

Below you will see four words and three of their codes. One of the codes is missing. Using the same code, convert the word or number below. Write the answer in the brackets or mark the appropriate box on the multiple choice answer sheet.

CARE   SOCK   RENT   ROSE
9865   6874   7395

Find the word for the code **795365**   (_____)

Daily Test 17

Score. _____

Question 1

In the question below, the three words in the second group should go together in the same way as the three in the first group. Find the missing word from the second group and write it in the space provided or mark the appropriate box on the multiple choice answer sheet.

toast   [shout]   south

bails [_____] ladle

Question 2

In this question you need to find the number that should appear in the brackets and completes the sum correctly. Write this number in the space provided or mark the appropriate box on the multiple choice answer sheet.

106 - 19 - 21 = 2 x 3 x (_____)

Question 3

In this question the numbers in each group are related in the same way. You must find the missing number in the third group and write it in the space provided or mark the appropriate box on the multiple choice answer sheet.

(7 [9] 25)   (18 [11] 40)

(16 [___] 36)

Question 4

In the sentence below, one word, which is in capitals, has had **three consecutive** letters taken out. These **three** letters will make one correctly spelt word without changing their order. Write the **three-letter** word in the space provided or mark the appropriate box on the multiple choice answer sheet.

The pictures hung around the walls of the **GERY**.

(_____)

Question 5

Below you will see four words and three of their codes. One of the codes is missing. Using the same code, convert the word or number below. Write the answer in the brackets or mark the appropriate box on the multiple choice answer sheet.

WASH   BEAT   DAWB   SHED
8254   3782   9571

Find the code for the word **BASHED** (_____)

Question 6

In the question below, **one** letter from the word on the left must be moved into the word on the right to make **two** new words. The letters must not be re-arranged. **Both** new words must make sense.
Write the correct letter in the space provided or mark the appropriate box on the multiple choice answer sheet.

CLAMP   PATH   (____)

Question 7

In this question you must find two words, **one** from each group, that are the **closest in meaning**.
Underline each of these two words or mark the appropriate boxes on the multiple choice answer sheet

(divide   subtract   multiply)

(attach   attract   split)

Question 8

In this question find the **two** words, **one** from each group that will complete the sentence in the best way.
Underline one word from each group or mark the appropriate boxes on the multiple choice answer sheet.

Duck is to (drake, avoid, pond)

as hen is to (chicken, cockerel, egg).

Question 9

In each question below, letters stand for numbers. Work out the answer to the sum and write its **letter** in the brackets or mark the appropriate box on the multiple choice answer sheet.

A = 5, B = 10, C = 2, D = 15, E = 7,

B x E ÷ A - E = (____)

Question 10

A B C D E F G H I J K L M N O P Q R S T U V W X Y Z

In this question a word has been written in code. An example has been worked out for you. You must now work out the missing word using the same code. Write the word in the space provided or mark the appropriate box on the multiple choice answer sheet.

If the code for **MILE** is **IKHG**

what does **LQOV** mean? (_____)

Daily Test 18

Question 1

In the question below, find one letter that will complete the word in front of the brackets and begin the word after the brackets.
The same letter must fit into both sets of brackets.
Write the letter on the answer sheet or mark the appropriate box on the multiple choice answer sheet.

PAI (___) AIL : STA (___) OCK

Question 2

In this question you need to find the number that should appear in the brackets and will continue the series in the most sensible way. Write this number in the space provided or mark the appropriate box on the multiple choice answer sheet.

2,   15,   3,   14,   5,   12,   8,   (____)

Question 3

In the sentence below, a word of four letters is hidden at the end of one word and the beginning of the next word.
Underline the **pair** of words that contain the hidden word or mark the appropriate box on the multiple choice answer sheet.

Claire's piano teacher was very pleased.

Question 4

A B C D E F G H I J K L M N O P Q R S T U V W X Y Z

In the question below, find the pair of letters that will complete the sentence in the best way and write the correct answer in the answer box or mark the appropriate box on the multiple choice answer sheet.

SL is to **PN**

as **RG** is to (_____)

Question 5

In the question below, there are two pairs of words. You must find the word from the list that will go equally well with both pairs of words in the brackets.
Underline this word or mark the appropriate box on the multiple choice answer sheet.

QUICK   PROMPT   EXPRESS   CHAT   CONVERSE

(SPEAK   STATE)   (FAST   RAPID)

Question 6

In this question there are three pairs of words. You must complete the third pair in the same way as the first two pairs. Write the correct word in the space provided or mark the appropriate box on the multiple choice answer sheet.

(remove, ever)   (danger, read)

(sachet, _____)

Question 7

In the question below, find two words, **one** from each group, that are the **most opposite in meaning**.
Underline each of these two words or mark the appropriate boxes on the multiple choice answer sheet

(imitate   start   illegal)

(begin   benign   lawful)

Question 8

In the question below, find the **two** words that are **different** from the other three and **underline** them on the answer sheet or mark the appropriate box on the multiple choice answer sheet.

misplace   mislead   lose   fool   mislay

Question 9

A B C D E F G H I J K L M N O P Q R S T U V W X Y Z

In this question you need to find the pair of letters that will complete the sequence in the best way and write the correct answer in the answer box or mark the appropriate box on the multiple choice answer sheet.

CD,   EE,   GG,   IJ,   KN,   (_____)

Question 10

In the question below, choose **two** words, **one** from each set, that will together make **one** correctly spelt word. You may not change the order of the letters.
The word from the set on the top always comes first.
Underline the two words or mark the appropriate boxes on the multiple choice answer sheet.

(smile   mouth   grin)

(part   full   piece)

Daily Test 19

Question 1

In the question below, the three words in the second group should go together in the same way as the three in the first group. Find the missing word from the second group and write it in the space provided or mark the appropriate box on the multiple choice answer sheet.

least   [slime]   times

horse [_____] hover

Question 2

In this question you need to find the number that should appear in the brackets and completes the sum correctly. Write this number in the space provided or mark the appropriate box on the multiple choice answer sheet.

$$103 - 25 - 28 = 14 + 16 + (\_\_\_\_\_)$$

Question 3

In this question the numbers in each group are related in the same way. You must find the missing number in the third group and write it in the space provided or mark the appropriate box on the multiple choice answer sheet.

(6 [19] 7)   (9 [29] 11)

(11 [___] 9)

Question 4

In the sentence below, one word, which is in capitals, has had **three consecutive** letters taken out. These **three** letters will make one correctly spelt word without changing their order. Write the **three-letter** word in the space provided or mark the appropriate box on the multiple choice answer sheet.

Sally and her friends go to **BRIES** on a Friday.

Answer _____

Question 5

Below you will see four words and three of their codes. One of the codes is missing. Using the same code, convert the word or number below. Write the answer in the brackets or mark the appropriate box on the multiple choice answer sheet.

SNUG   NEWT   PENS   PUNT
3479   1742   4862

Find the code for the word **WEEPS** (_____)

Question 6

In the question below, **one** letter from the word on the left must be moved into the word on the right to make **two** new words. The letters must not be re-arranged. **Both** new words must make sense. Write the correct letter in the space provided or mark the appropriate box on the multiple choice answer sheet.

WEARY   CLAN   (____)

Question 7

In this question you must find two words, **one** from each group, that are the **closest in meaning**. **Underline** each of these two words or mark the appropriate boxes on the multiple choice answer sheet

(disperse   converge   require)

(scatter   hesitate   enforce)

Question 8

In this question find the **two** words, **one** from each group that will complete the sentence in the best way. **Underline** one word from each group or mark the appropriate boxes on the multiple choice answer sheet.

Mane is to (lion, main, chief)

as paws is to (swap, cease, pause).

Question 9

In each question below, letters stand for numbers. Work out the answer to the sum and write its **letter** in the brackets or mark the appropriate box on the multiple choice answer sheet.

A = 100   B = 25,   C = 5,   D = 50,   E = 10,

$$A \div E + C + E = (\_\_\_\_)$$

Question 10

A B C D E F G H I J K L M N O P Q R S T U V W X Y Z

In this question a word has been written in code. An example has been worked out for you. You must now work out the missing word using the same code. Write the word in the space provided or mark the appropriate box on the multiple choice answer sheet.

If the code for **PACK** is **QYFG**,

what does **CCDN** mean? (_____)

Daily Test 20

Question 1

In the question below, find one letter that will complete the word in front of the brackets and begin the word after the brackets.
The same letter must fit into both sets of brackets.
Write the letter on the answer sheet or mark the appropriate box on the multiple choice answer sheet.

SLU (___) USH   :   SIN (___) OAL

Question 2

In this question you need to find the number that should appear in the brackets and will continue the series in the most sensible way. Write this number in the space provided or mark the appropriate box on the multiple choice answer sheet.

19,   24,   28,   33,   37,   42,   (____)

Question 3

In the sentence below, a word of four letters is hidden at the end of one word and the beginning of the next word. **Underline** the **pair** of words that contain the hidden word or mark the appropriate box on the multiple choice answer sheet.

The baker baked bread and cakes.

Question 4

A B C D E F G H I J K L M N O P Q R S T U V W X Y Z

In the question below, find the pair of letters that will complete the sentence in the best way and write the correct answer in the answer box or mark the appropriate box on the multiple choice answer sheet.

HS is to **GQ**
as **RI** is to (_____)

Question 5

In the question below, there are two pairs of words. You must find the word from the list that will go equally well with both pairs of words in the brackets.
Underline this word or mark the appropriate box on the multiple choice answer sheet.

MAKE   MOULD   CARVE   MILDEW   ROT

(FUNGUS   GROWTH)   (SHAPE   SCULPT)

Question 6

In this question there are three pairs of words. You must complete the third pair in the same way as the first two pairs. Write the correct word in the space provided or mark the appropriate box on the multiple choice answer sheet.

(railway, wail)   (develop, love)

(charter, _____)

Question 7

In the question below, find two words, **one** from each group, that are the **most opposite in meaning**.
Underline each of these two words or mark the appropriate boxes on the multiple choice answer sheet

(destroy   deter   dismiss)
(disobey   create   linger)

Question 8

In the question below, find the **two** words that are **different** from the other three and **underline** them on the answer sheet or mark the appropriate box on the multiple choice answer sheet.

tie   scarf   bind   close   tether

Question 9

A B C D E F G H I J K L M N O P Q R S T U V W X Y Z

In this question you need to find the pair of letters that will complete the sequence in the best way and write the correct answer in the answer box or mark the appropriate box on the multiple choice answer sheet.

FH,   HJ,   JL,   LN,   NP,   (_____)

Question 10

In the question below, choose **two** words, **one** from each set, that will together make **one** correctly spelt word. You may not change the order of the letters.
The word from the set on the top always comes first.
Underline the two words or mark the appropriate boxes on the multiple choice answer sheet.

(gasp   puff   blow)

(wing   in   red)

Multiple choice answer sheet.   Tests 1 to 4.

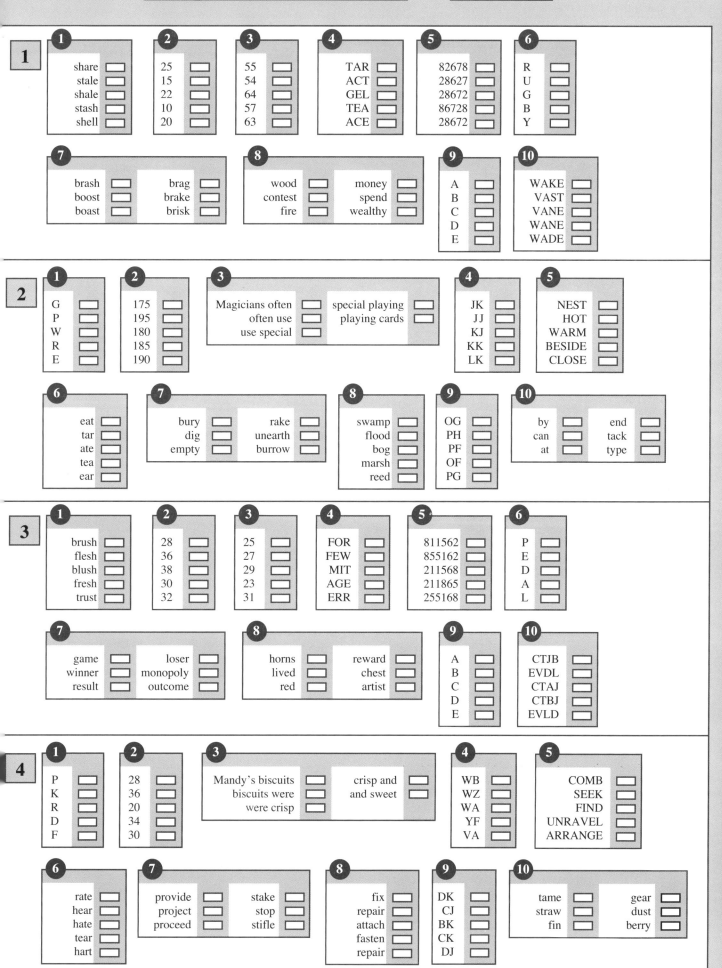

1

1
share ☐
stale ☐
shale ☐
stash ☐
shell ☐

2
25 ☐
15 ☐
22 ☐
10 ☐
20 ☐

3
55 ☐
54 ☐
64 ☐
57 ☐
63 ☐

4
TAR ☐
ACT ☐
GEL ☐
TEA ☐
ACE ☐

5
82678 ☐
28627 ☐
28672 ☐
86728 ☐
28672 ☐

6
R ☐
U ☐
G ☐
B ☐
Y

7
brash ☐   brag ☐
boost ☐   brake ☐
boast ☐   brisk ☐

8
wood ☐   money ☐
contest ☐   spend ☐
fire ☐   wealthy ☐

9
A ☐
B ☐
C ☐
D ☐
E ☐

10
WAKE ☐
VAST ☐
VANE ☐
WANE ☐
WADE ☐

2

1
G ☐
P ☐
W ☐
R ☐
E ☐

2
175 ☐
195 ☐
180 ☐
185 ☐
190 ☐

3
Magicians often ☐   special playing ☐
often use ☐   playing cards ☐
use special ☐

4
JK ☐
JJ ☐
KJ ☐
KK ☐
LK ☐

5
NEST ☐
HOT ☐
WARM ☐
BESIDE ☐
CLOSE ☐

6
eat ☐
tar ☐
ate ☐
tea ☐
ear ☐

7
bury ☐   rake ☐
dig ☐   unearth ☐
empty ☐   burrow ☐

8
swamp ☐
flood ☐
bog ☐
marsh ☐
reed ☐

9
OG ☐
PH ☐
PF ☐
OF ☐
PG ☐

10
by ☐   end ☐
can ☐   tack ☐
at ☐   type ☐

3

1
brush ☐
flesh ☐
blush ☐
fresh ☐
trust ☐

2
28 ☐
36 ☐
38 ☐
30 ☐
32 ☐

3
25 ☐
27 ☐
29 ☐
23 ☐
31 ☐

4
FOR ☐
FEW ☐
MIT ☐
AGE ☐
ERR ☐

5
811562 ☐
855162 ☐
211568 ☐
211865 ☐
255168 ☐

6
P ☐
E ☐
D ☐
A ☐
L

7
game ☐   loser ☐
winner ☐   monopoly ☐
result ☐   outcome ☐

8
horns ☐   reward ☐
lived ☐   chest ☐
red ☐   artist ☐

9
A ☐
B ☐
C ☐
D ☐
E ☐

10
CTJB ☐
EVDL ☐
CTAJ ☐
CTBJ ☐
EVLD ☐

4

1
P ☐
K ☐
R ☐
D ☐
F ☐

2
28 ☐
36 ☐
20 ☐
34 ☐
30 ☐

3
Mandy's biscuits ☐   crisp and ☐
biscuits were ☐   and sweet ☐
were crisp ☐

4
WB ☐
WZ ☐
WA ☐
YF ☐
VA ☐

5
COMB ☐
SEEK ☐
FIND ☐
UNRAVEL ☐
ARRANGE ☐

6
rate ☐
hear ☐
hate ☐
tear ☐
hart ☐

7
provide ☐   stake ☐
project ☐   stop ☐
proceed ☐   stifle ☐

8
fix ☐
repair ☐
attach ☐
fasten ☐
repair ☐

9
DK ☐
CJ ☐
BK ☐
CK ☐
DJ ☐

10
tame ☐   gear ☐
straw ☐   dust ☐
fin ☐   berry ☐

Multiple choice answer sheet.   Tests 5 to 8.

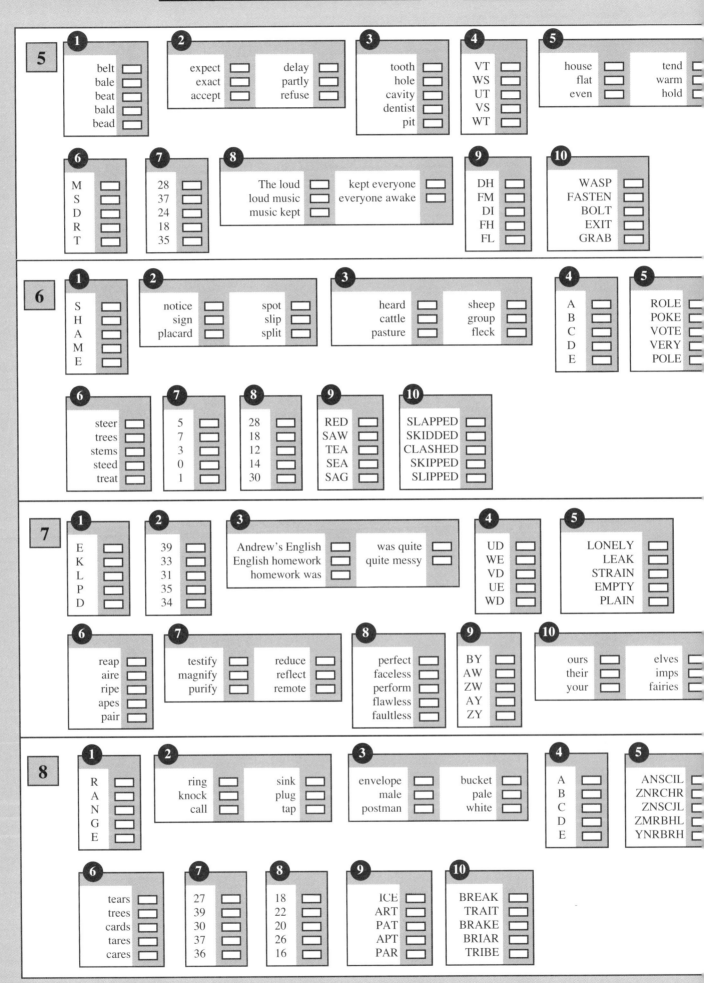

5

1
belt
bale
beat
bald
bead

2
expect   delay
exact   partly
accept   refuse

3
tooth
hole
cavity
dentist
pit

4
VT
WS
UT
VS
WT

5
house   tend
flat   warm
even   hold

6
M
S
D
R
T

7
28
37
24
18
35

8
The loud   kept everyone
loud music   everyone awake
music kept

9
DH
FM
DI
FH
FL

10
WASP
FASTEN
BOLT
EXIT
GRAB

6

1
S
H
A
M
E

2
notice   spot
sign   slip
placard   split

3
heard   sheep
cattle   group
pasture   fleck

4
A
B
C
D
E

5
ROLE
POKE
VOTE
VERY
POLE

6
steer
trees
stems
steed
treat

7
5
7
3
0
1

8
28
18
12
14
30

9
RED
SAW
TEA
SEA
SAG

10
SLAPPED
SKIDDED
CLASHED
SKIPPED
SLIPPED

7

1
E
K
L
P
D

2
39
33
31
35
34

3
Andrew's English   was quite
English homework   quite messy
homework was

4
UD
WE
VD
UE
WD

5
LONELY
LEAK
STRAIN
EMPTY
PLAIN

6
reap
aire
ripe
apes
pair

7
testify   reduce
magnify   reflect
purify   remote

8
perfect
faceless
perform
flawless
faultless

9
BY
AW
ZW
AY
ZY

10
ours   elves
their   imps
your   fairies

8

1
R
A
N
G
E

2
ring   sink
knock   plug
call   tap

3
envelope   bucket
male   pale
postman   white

4
A
B
C
D
E

5
ANSCIL
ZNRCHR
ZNSCJL
ZMRBHL
YNRBRH

6
tears
trees
cards
tares
cares

7
27
39
30
37
36

8
18
22
20
26
16

9
ICE
ART
PAT
APT
PAR

10
BREAK
TRAIT
BRAKE
BRIAR
TRIBE

Multiple choice answer sheet.   Tests 9 to 12.

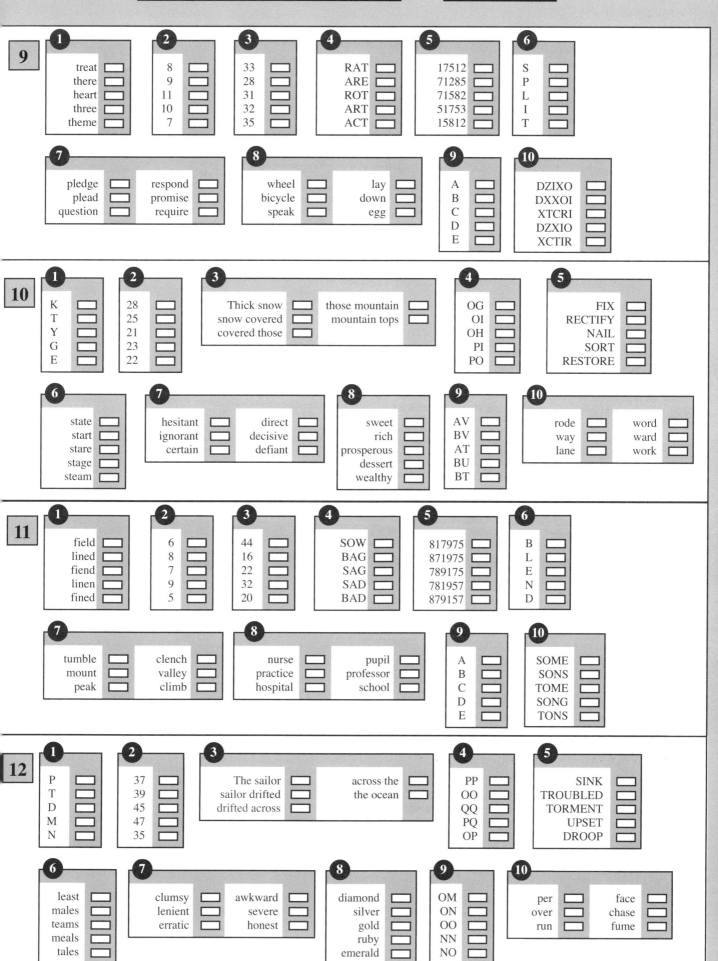

9

1
treat
there
heart
three
theme

2
8
9
11
10
7

3
33
28
31
32
35

4
RAT
ARE
ROT
ART
ACT

5
17512
71285
71582
51753
15812

6
S
P
L
I
T

7
pledge   respond
plead   promise
question require

8
wheel   lay
bicycle   down
speak   egg

9
A
B
C
D
E

10
DZIXO
DXXOI
XTCRI
DZXIO
XCTIR

10

1
K
T
Y
G
E

2
28
25
21
23
22

3
Thick snow   those mountain
snow covered   mountain tops
covered those

4
OG
OI
OH
PI
PO

5
FIX
RECTIFY
NAIL
SORT
RESTORE

6
state
start
stare
stage
steam

7
hesitant   direct
ignorant   decisive
certain   defiant

8
sweet
rich
prosperous
dessert
wealthy

9
AV
BV
AT
BU
BT

10
rode   word
way   ward
lane   work

11

1
field
lined
fiend
linen
fined

2
6
8
7
9
5

3
44
16
22
32
20

4
SOW
BAG
SAG
SAD
BAD

5
817975
871975
789175
781957
879157

6
B
L
E
N
D

7
tumble   clench
mount   valley
peak   climb

8
nurse   pupil
practice professor
hospital school

9
A
B
C
D
E

10
SOME
SONS
TOME
SONG
TONS

12

1
P
T
D
M
N

2
37
39
45
47
35

3
The sailor   across the
sailor drifted the ocean
drifted across

4
PP
OO
QQ
PQ
OP

5
SINK
TROUBLED
TORMENT
UPSET
DROOP

6
least
males
teams
meals
tales

7
clumsy   awkward
lenient severe
erratic honest

8
diamond
silver
gold
ruby
emerald

9
OM
ON
OO
NN
NO

10
per   face
over   chase
run   fume

Multiple choice answer sheet.   Tests 13 to 16.

13

1
- ease ☐
- teas ☐
- teak ☐
- task ☐
- east ☐

2
- ready ☐
- steady ☐
- charge ☐
- unstable ☐
- fixed ☐
- faulty ☐

3
- melt ☐
- boil ☐
- defrost ☐
- heat ☐
- thaw ☐

4
- YP ☐
- ZP ☐
- ZQ ☐
- ZO ☐
- YQ ☐

5
- break ☐
- snap ☐
- cut ☐
- though ☐
- through ☐
- tough ☐

6
- N ☐
- K ☐
- Y ☐
- S ☐
- P ☐

7
- 135 ☐
- 140 ☐
- 125 ☐
- 160 ☐
- 150 ☐

8
- Keep calm ☐
- calm when ☐
- when the ☐
- the alarm ☐
- alarm rings ☐

9
- KI ☐
- EJ ☐
- KJ ☐
- EL ☐
- EI ☐

10
- ATTACHED ☐
- SPRING ☐
- SKIP ☐
- BONDED ☐
- BOUND ☐

14

1
- L ☐
- A ☐
- N ☐
- C ☐
- E ☐

2
- mystery ☐
- confess ☐
- mimic ☐
- confuse ☐
- puzzle ☐
- mystify ☐

3
- cease ☐
- grab ☐
- start ☐
- dear ☐
- heap ☐
- bird ☐

4
- A ☐
- B ☐
- C ☐
- D ☐
- E ☐

5
- UXIXPR ☐
- IHPXPR ☐
- IHIXRP ☐
- IHPXEV ☐
- UXIXRP ☐

6
- dears ☐
- scare ☐
- sides ☐
- score ☐
- dares ☐

7
- 13 ☐
- 9 ☐
- 15 ☐
- 12 ☐
- 11 ☐

8
- 27 ☐
- 29 ☐
- 45 ☐
- 25 ☐
- 55 ☐

9
- RAP ☐
- LED ☐
- OLD ☐
- LID ☐
- RUN ☐

10
- MATTER ☐
- ROTATE ☐
- RATHER ☐
- MOTHER ☐
- HEATER ☐

15

1
- F ☐
- R ☐
- L ☐
- N ☐
- D ☐

2
- 33 ☐
- 34 ☐
- 36 ☐
- 35 ☐
- 32 ☐

3
- Some genies ☐
- genies live ☐
- live inside ☐
- inside old ☐
- old lamps ☐

4
- FM ☐
- GL ☐
- HY ☐
- HM ☐
- GM ☐

5
- STRIP ☐
- FIGHT ☐
- STRING ☐
- ROW ☐
- QUEUE ☐

6
- dame ☐
- name ☐
- game ☐
- came ☐
- fame ☐

7
- bright ☐
- occupy ☐
- seldom ☐
- often ☐
- rare ☐
- quietly ☐

8
- begin ☐
- end ☐
- start ☐
- finish ☐
- conclude ☐

9
- OV ☐
- QU ☐
- PT ☐
- OU ☐
- PU ☐

10
- short ☐
- rum ☐
- flow ☐
- wing ☐
- age ☐
- here ☐

16

1
- H ☐
- E ☐
- A ☐
- R ☐
- T ☐

2
- remind ☐
- remove ☐
- remedy ☐
- placed ☐
- cure ☐
- behind ☐

3
- mix ☐
- choose ☐
- shovel ☐
- shift ☐
- house ☐
- motivate ☐

4
- A ☐
- B ☐
- C ☐
- D ☐
- E ☐

5
- MIMES ☐
- GIANT ☐
- MINCE ☐
- GIRLS ☐
- MINER ☐

6
- toads ☐
- trade ☐
- tread ☐
- treat ☐
- toast ☐

7
- 14 ☐
- 16 ☐
- 15 ☐
- 13 ☐
- 12 ☐

8
- 49 ☐
- 51 ☐
- 45 ☐
- 47 ☐
- 42 ☐

9
- PIN ☐
- TEA ☐
- PEN ☐
- RAP ☐
- EAT ☐

10
- CREASE ☐
- RACERS ☐
- SCARES ☐
- CROCKS ☐
- ROCKER ☐

Multiple choice answer sheet.   Tests 17 to 20.

17

1
- label ☐
- leads ☐
- bales ☐
- loads ☐
- beads ☐

2
- 7 ☐
- 13 ☐
- 9 ☐
- 11 ☐
- 8 ☐

3
- 25 ☐
- 10 ☐
- 20 ☐
- 27 ☐
- 16 ☐

4
- ALL ☐
- RED ☐
- MAT ☐
- HUT ☐
- PUT ☐

5
- 657245 ☐
- 987542 ☐
- 618547 ☐
- 978254 ☐
- 675245 ☐

6
- C ☐
- L ☐
- A ☐
- M ☐
- P

7
- divide ☐
- subtract ☐
- multiply ☐
- attach ☐
- attract ☐
- split ☐

8
- drake ☐
- avoid ☐
- pond ☐
- chicken ☐
- cockerel ☐
- egg ☐

9
- A ☐
- B ☐
- C ☐
- D ☐
- E ☐

10
- HAMS ☐
- PAST ☐
- POSE ☐
- HOLE ☐
- POST ☐

18

1
- D ☐
- R ☐
- N ☐
- L ☐
- W ☐

2
- 10 ☐
- 11 ☐
- 12 ☐
- 9 ☐
- 8 ☐

3
- Claire's piano ☐
- piano teacher ☐
- teacher was ☐
- was very ☐
- very pleased ☐

4
- OI ☐
- UJ ☐
- OJ ☐
- UE ☐
- UI ☐

5
- QUICK ☐
- PROMPT ☐
- EXPRESS ☐
- CHAT ☐
- CONVERSE ☐

6
- teas ☐
- seat ☐
- chat ☐
- each ☐
- heat ☐

7
- imitate ☐
- start ☐
- illegal ☐
- begin ☐
- benign ☐
- lawful ☐

8
- misplace ☐
- mislead ☐
- lose ☐
- fool ☐
- mislay ☐

9
- NS ☐
- MT ☐
- MR ☐
- MS ☐
- NT ☐

10
- smile ☐
- mouth ☐
- grin ☐
- part ☐
- full ☐
- piece ☐

19

1
- shoes ☐
- verse ☐
- sheer ☐
- rover ☐
- shove ☐

2
- 21 ☐
- 23 ☐
- 20 ☐
- 25 ☐
- 29 ☐

3
- 31 ☐
- 29 ☐
- 25 ☐
- 20 ☐
- 40 ☐

4
- ROW ☐
- ORE ☐
- RAP ☐
- ART ☐
- OWN ☐

5
- 67714 ☐
- 57723 ☐
- 68813 ☐
- 57714 ☐
- 58814 ☐

6
- W ☐
- E ☐
- A ☐
- R ☐
- Y

7
- disperse ☐
- converge ☐
- require ☐
- scatter ☐
- hesitate ☐
- enforce ☐

8
- lion ☐
- main ☐
- chief ☐
- swap ☐
- cease ☐
- pause ☐

9
- A ☐
- B ☐
- C ☐
- D ☐
- E ☐

10
- BEET ☐
- BEAD ☐
- BEAT ☐
- BEAR ☐
- BEER ☐

20

1
- M ☐
- G ☐
- R ☐
- S ☐
- D ☐

2
- 45 ☐
- 44 ☐
- 46 ☐
- 48 ☐
- 47 ☐

3
- The baker ☐
- baker baked ☐
- baked bread ☐
- bread and ☐
- and cakes ☐

4
- RH ☐
- QG ☐
- PI ☐
- PG ☐
- QH ☐

5
- MAKE ☐
- MOULD ☐
- CARVE ☐
- MILDEW ☐
- ROT ☐

6
- tare ☐
- tear ☐
- rate ☐
- arch ☐
- each ☐

7
- destroy ☐
- deter ☐
- dismiss ☐
- disobey ☐
- create ☐
- linger ☐

8
- tie ☐
- scarf ☐
- bind ☐
- close ☐
- tether ☐

9
- PR ☐
- PS ☐
- PT ☐
- OR ☐
- OS ☐

10
- gasp ☐
- puff ☐
- blow ☐
- wing ☐
- in ☐
- red ☐

Answers

	Test 1	Test 2	Test 3	Test 4	Test 5
1	shale	W	fresh	D	bald
2	20	185	28	36	accept / refuse
3	64	Magicians often (soft)	23	crisp and (span)	tooth / dentist
4	ACT	JK	FOR	VA	VS
5	82678	CLOSE	855162	COMB	house hold
6	G	Tar	D	rate	T
7	boast / brag	bury / unearth	result / outcome	proceed / stop	37
8	contest / wealthy	flood / reed	lived / reward	make / repair	music kept (sick)
9	B	PG	E	CJ	DH
10	WADE	at tack	EVDL	straw berry	BOLT

	Test 6	Test 7	Test 8	Test 9	Test 10
1	H	K	N	theme	G
2	notice / spot	34	knock / tap	8	21
3	cattle / sheep	quite messy (item)	male / pale	32	mountain tops (into)
4	A	VD	E	ACT	OH
5	POLE	EMPTY	ZMRBHL	71582	FIX
6	trees	RIPE	cards	L	state
7	0	magnify / reduce	37	pledge / promise	hesitant / decisive
8	14	faceless / perform	22	speak / lay	sweet / dessert
9	SAG	AW	ART	A	BU
10	SKIDDED	ours elves	BREAK	XTCRI	way ward

	Test 11	Test 12	Test 13	Test 14	Test 15
1	fiend	P	east	N	L
2	5	47	steady / unstable	mystery / puzzle	33
3	32	sailor drifted (lord)	boil / heat	start / dear	live inside (vein)
4	BAD	PP	YP	C	GL
5	871975	UPSET	break through	UXIXPR	ROW
6	N	tales	P	scare	CAME
7	mount / climb	lenient / severe	125	13	seldom / often
8	hospital / school	silver / gold	the alarm (heal)	45	begin / start
9	C	OM	KI	LID	OU
10	SONG	per fume	BOUND	MOTHER	short age

	Test 16	Test 17	Test 18	Test 19	Test 20
1	T	leads	R	Shove	G
2	remedy / cure	11	9	20	46
3	choose / shift	10	piano teacher (note)	31	baker baked (kerb)
4	A	ALL	OI	OWN	QG
5	MINER	978254	EXPRESS	68813	MOULD
6	Trade	C	teas	E	tear
7	15	divide / split	illegal / lawful	disperse / scatter	destroy / create
8	51	drake / cockerel	mislead / fool	main / pause	scarf / close
9	PEN	E	MS	B	PR
10	CREASE	POST	mouth piece	BEAR	puff in